At Home

written by Dean Turner

photographs by Ken Kinzie

Harcourt

Orlando   Boston   Dallas   Chicago   San Diego

Visit *The Learning Site!*

www.harcourtschool.com

Mom

Dad

Sister

Brother

Birdie

Home

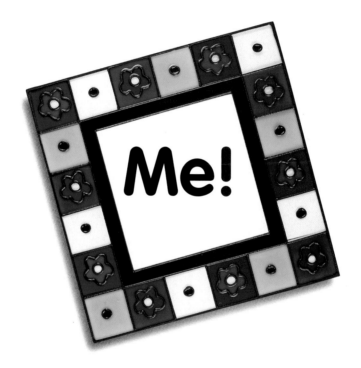

Acknowledgments:
Page 12 John M. Roberts/The Stock Market; Page 14 Barbara Filet/Tony Stone Images.
All other photographs by Ken Kinzie ©Harcourt

Printed in the United States of America

ISBN 0-15-314277-4

4 5 6 7 8 9 10 060 02 01 00